I'M DIRTY!

KATE & JIM
McMULLAN

SCHOLASTIC INC.
New York Toronto London Auckland Sydney
Mexico City New Delhi Hong Kong Buenos Aires

 • ISBN-13: 978-0-545-02955-1 • ISBN-10: 0-545-02955-4 • Published by Scholastic Inc., 557 Broadway, New York, NY 10012, by arrangement with HarperCollins Publishers.
12 11 10 9 8 7 6 5 4 3 2 1 7 8 9 10 11/0 • Printed in Mexico 49 • First Scholastic printing, September 2007 • Typography by Neil Swaab

For backhoe ace Michael Steiner

A great big load of thanks to the HarperCollins Crew:
Joanna Cotler, Justin Chanda, Alyson Day,
Neil Swaab, Ruiko Tokunaga, Karen Nagel, and Kathryn Silsand.
Also to Mindy Reyer, Jacqueline Moss, Peter Field,
and the kids at the Morris Center School;
Dan Steiger and Meridith Nadler;
Bill Villano at One Source Tools;
Antonio, Daphne, Gemma, and Paolo Caglioti;
and to my first-prize, cross-your-eyes Pippins,
Holly McGhee and Emily van Beek.

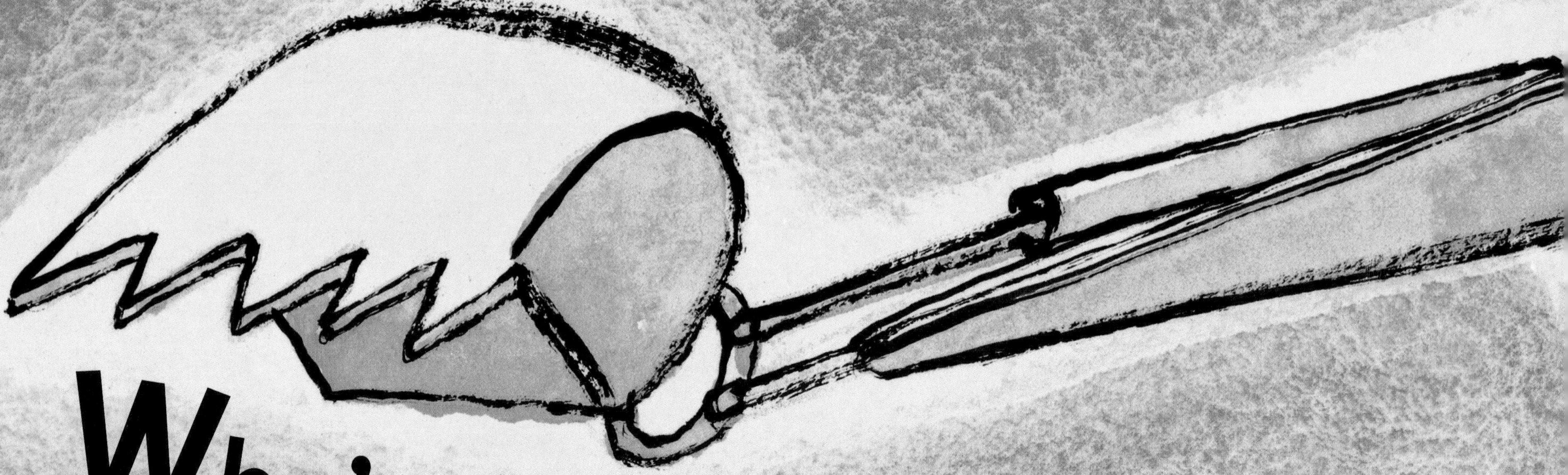

Who's got
a BOOM,
a dipper stick,
and a BUCKET
with a row of chompers?

ME!

And that's just my **REAR** end.

Up ***FRONT***,

I've got steel arms, hydraulic rams,

and a specialized,

maximized,

GIANT-SIZED

LOADER BUCKET.

Flatbed truck?

Get me to work.

Backhoe Loader, reporting for duty.

Cleaning up this mess? Easy as pie.
Make that a ***MUD*** pie.

ABOUT-FACE!

Down the ramp . . .

DON'T DUMP
NO DUMPING

Counting down
10 torn-up truck tires
9 fractured fans

what I'm cleaning up:
8 busted beach umbrellas
7 loused-up lawn chairs

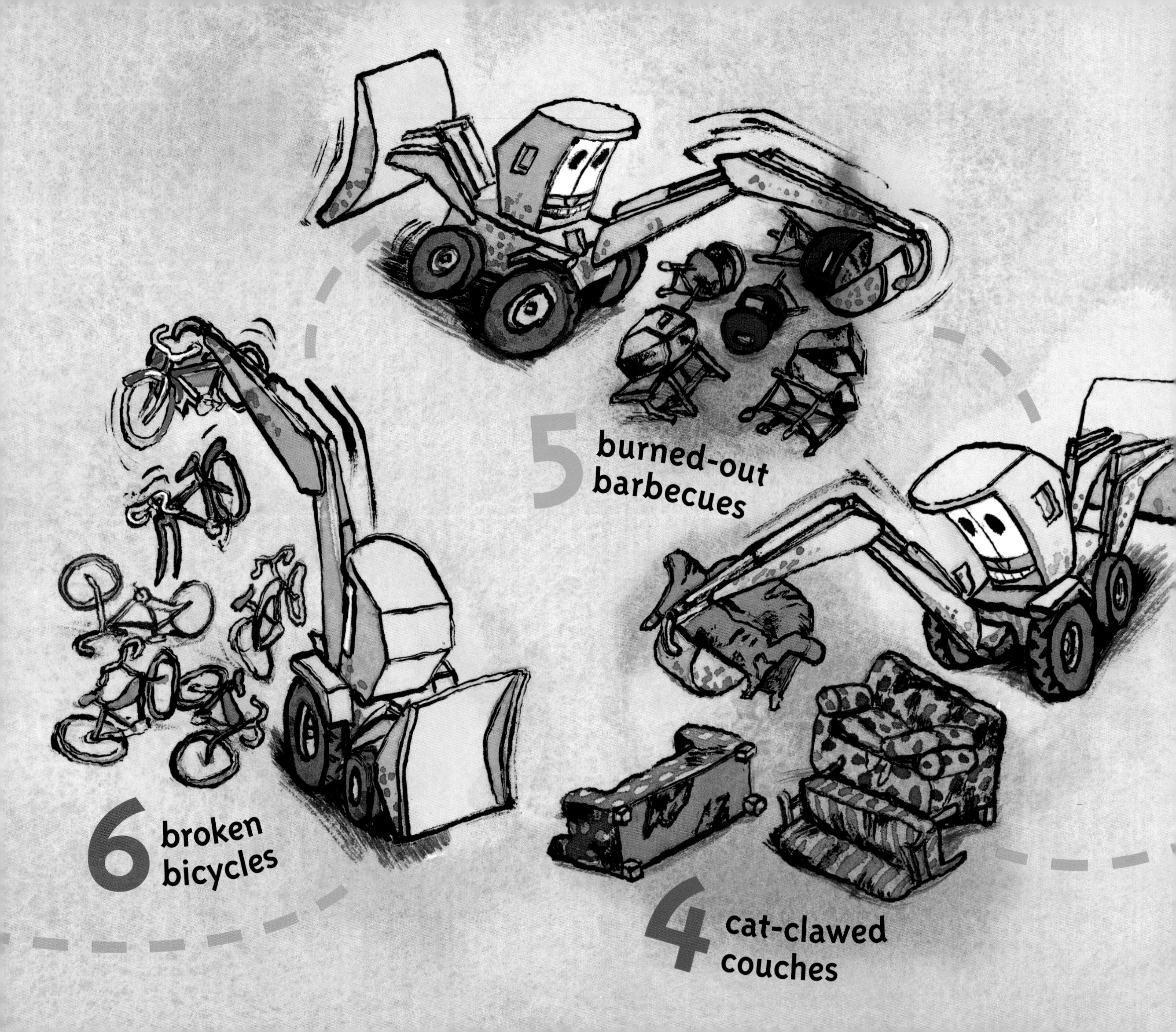
5 burned-out barbecues
6 broken bicycles
4 cat-clawed couches

1 wonky washing machine.
CLONK!
2 tossed-out toilet seats
3 scuffed-up signs
NO DUMPING
ON'T DUMP
$200 FINE FOR DUMPING

Dumpster time . . .

Hope ya
like Noise.
CLANK!
Rattle!

BANG!
BONG!
Bing!
BONG!
BANG!
Clunk!

On to the DIRTY part of the job.
Coming to take you out, Stumpie.

Stabilizer legs?
Take a stance.

Bucket? Bite the dirt.

Aw, Stumpie—loosen up.
Ugh!
Arrrrrrgh!
Mmmmmmmmmmmmmmpuh!

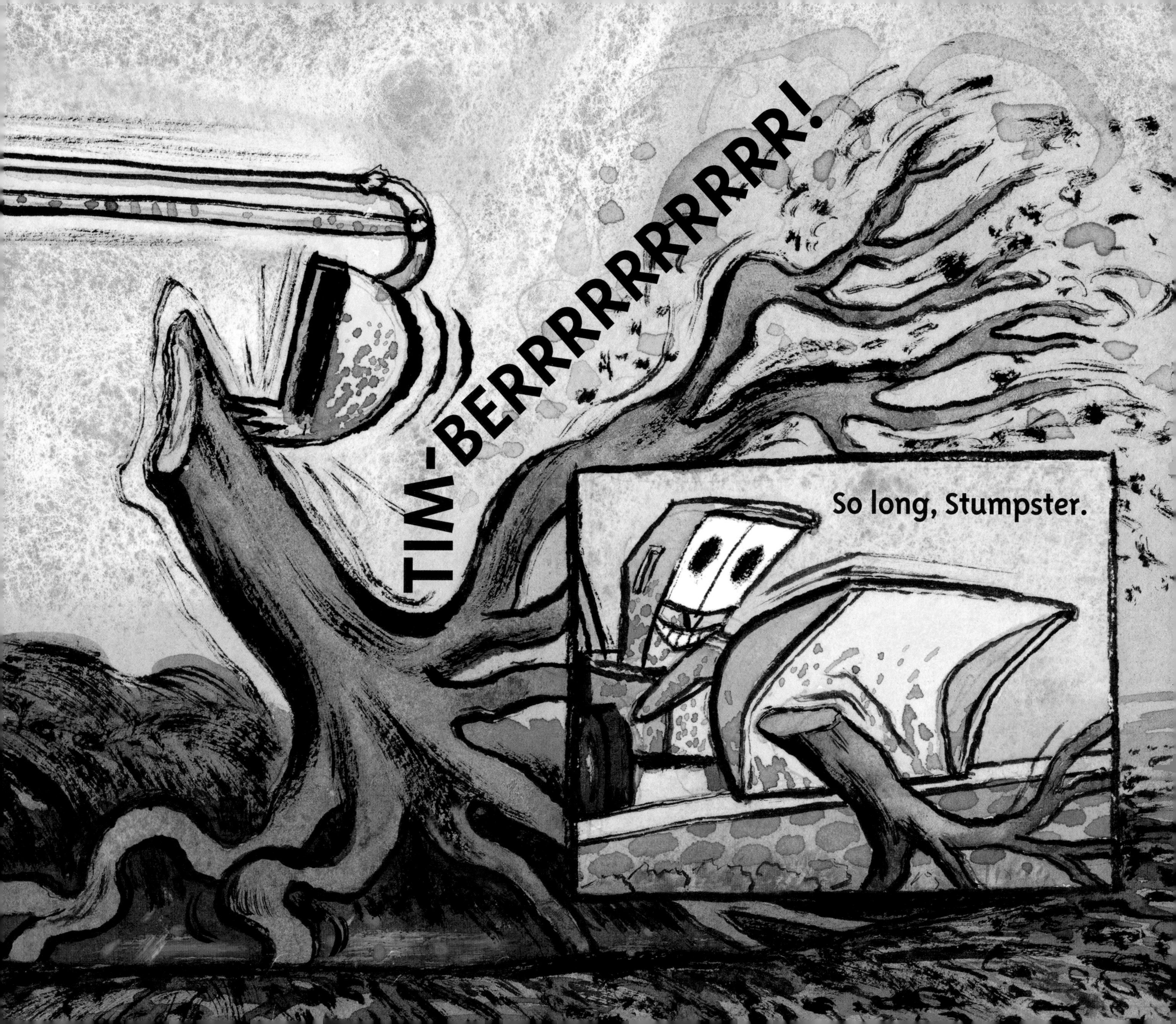
TIM-BERRRRRRRRRR!
So long, Stumpster.

Whew! I need a **bath**.
Make that a **MUD bath**.

Ahhhhhhhhh . . .
I just **love** my work.

Stuck in the muck? **NOT ME.**

Tires?

Do your thing.

Filling in the hole?
Piece of cake.

Make that a MUD cake with dirt sprinkles and a scoop of Rocky Road.
DIG IN!

I like things **smoooooooooth**,
so I shift it into R,
and back-drag the bucket over the dirt.

How's THAT for flat?

Backhoe Loader, signing off.

Have a
dirty day!

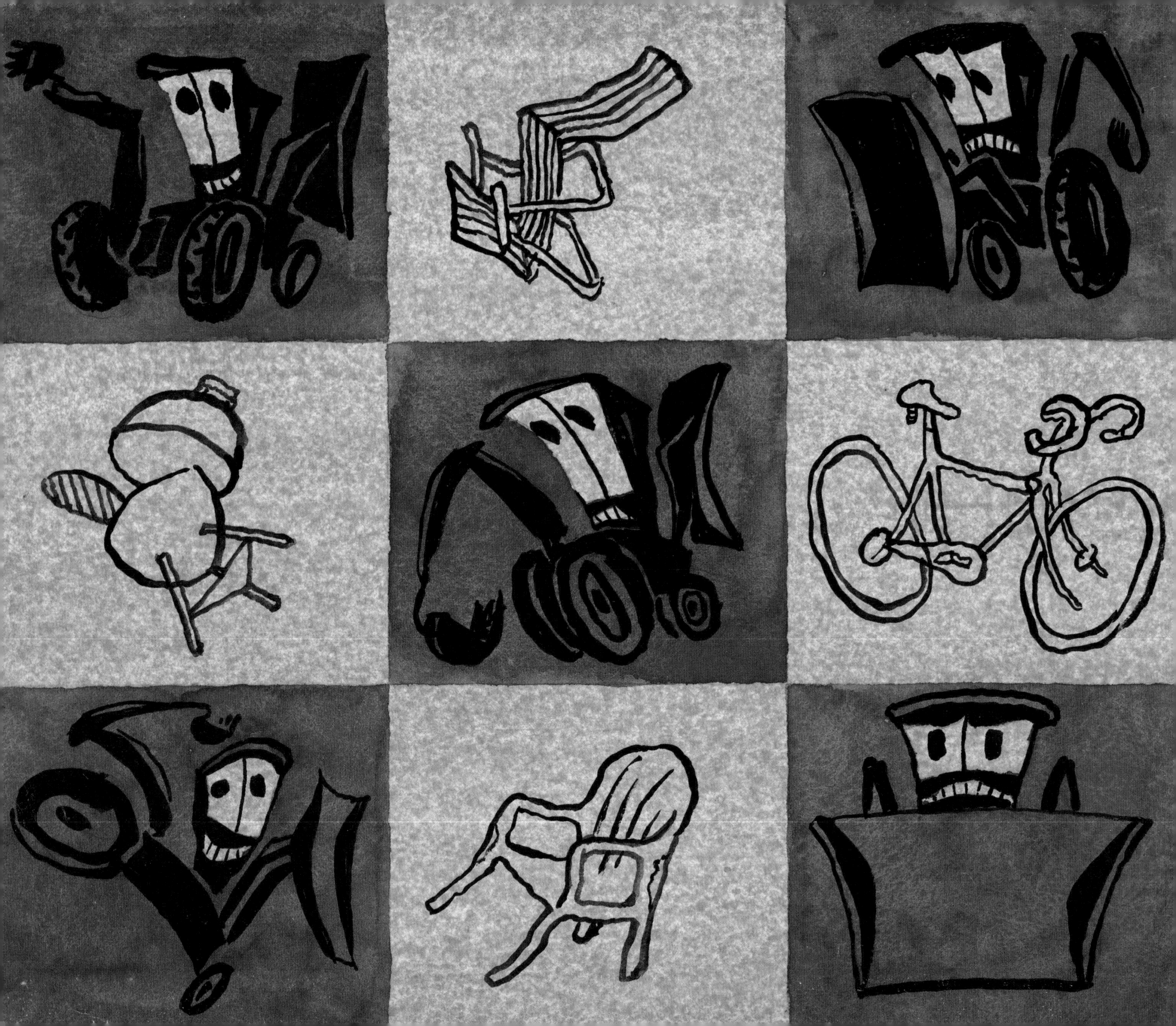